D1282520

EASTER COLOR BY NUMBER - A FUN AND CREATIVE WORKBOOK FOR THE HOLIDAYS WITH 30 CUTE DESIGNS

FOR KIDS AGES 4 TO 8

FUNKEY BOOKS

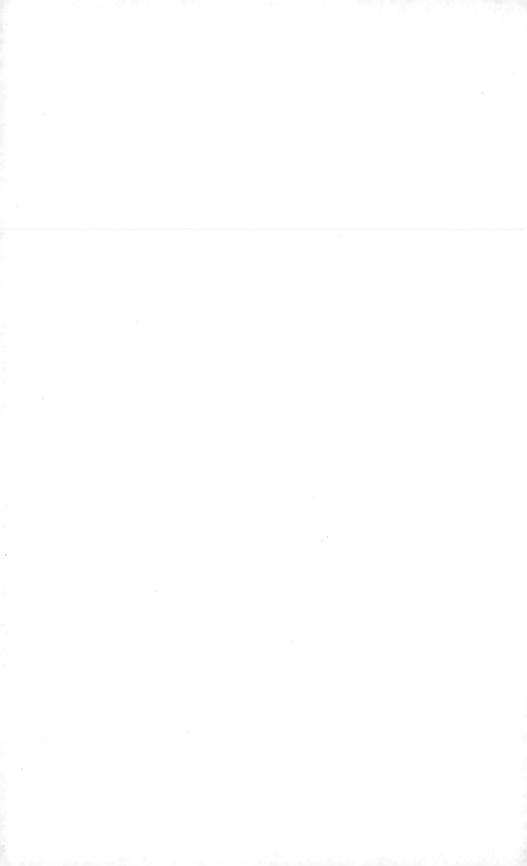

You can find more of our books
on Amazon!

Simply search for "Funkey Books"
on www.amazon.com.

Happy Easter _____!

(Insert your name here)

How nice that our little book has found its way to you! This is going to be an egg-cellent time!

Each picture in this book is divided into shapes and has a unique coloring key going along with it. The key is there to help you figure out which color each little field should have. If the color of pen number 1 is "blue", for example, every shape with the number 1 on it can be colored in blue.

Little tip: Don't press your coloured pencil as hard for the lighter colors as you would for the darker ones to achieve different color effects.

And, of course, we don't want to limit your imagination. So if you think that some elements would look nicer in a different color or if you don't have a specific color, don't worry: Just take another one and your picture will look just as beautiful!

Now bring each page to life with some color and enjoy with the Easter Bunny and his friends! :-)

Bonus Question:

How many easter eggs can you find inside this book?

——————

(Check your answer at the end of the book.)

Let's go!

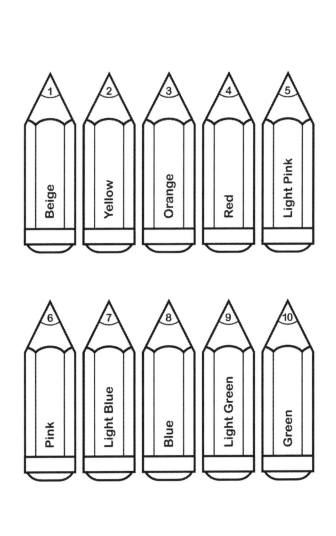

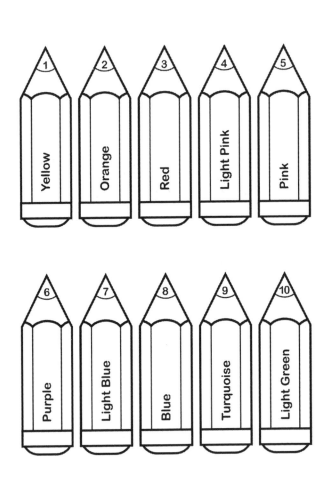

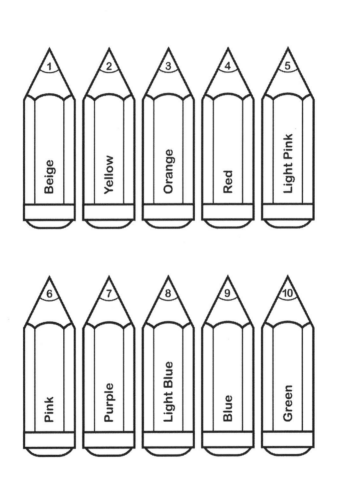

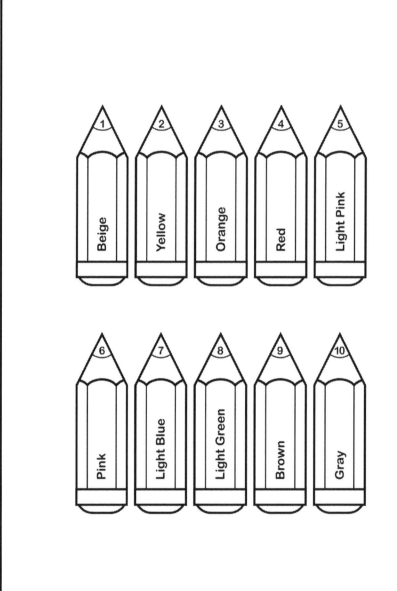

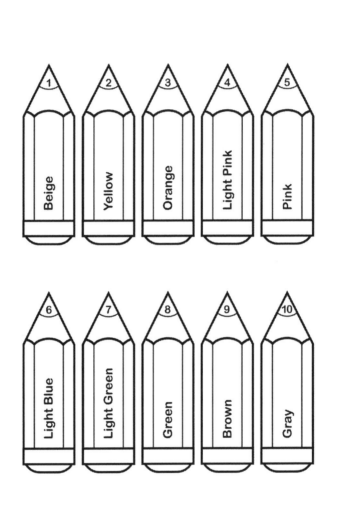

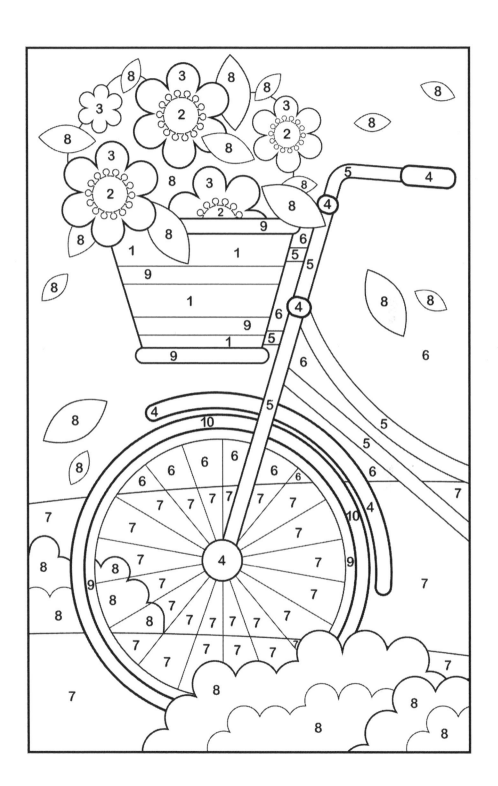

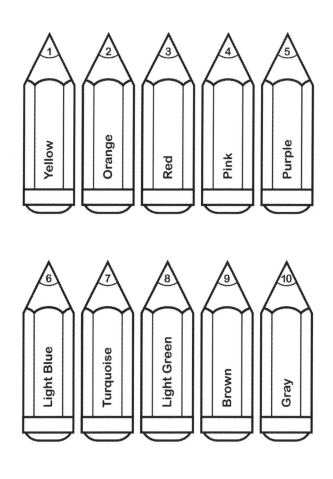

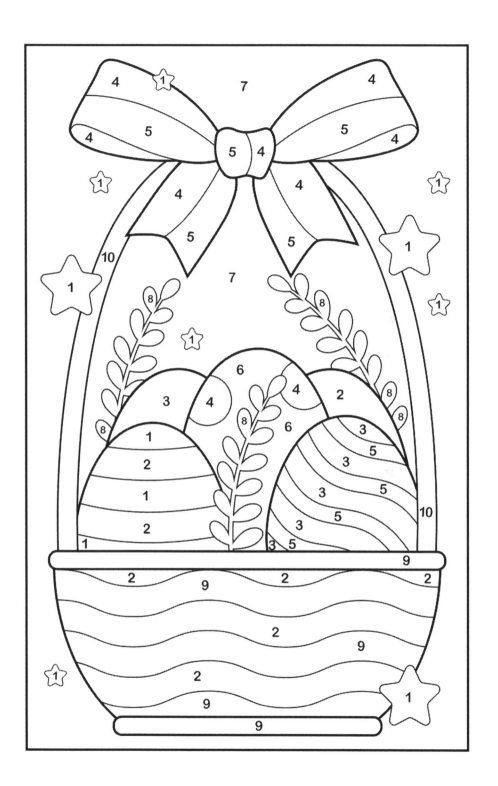

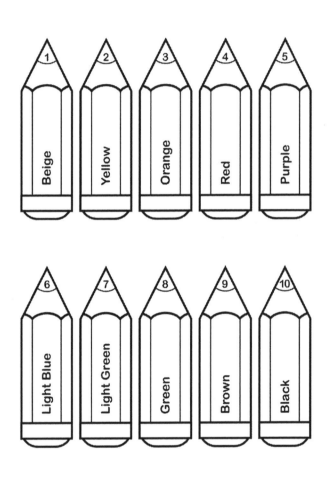

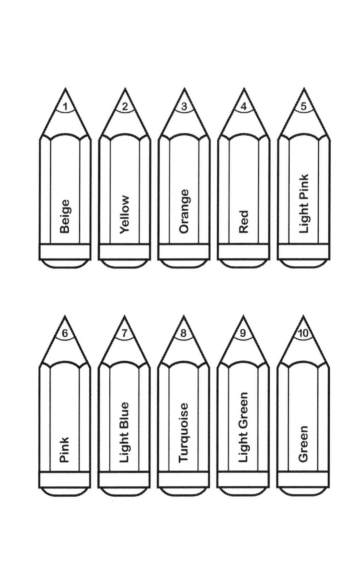

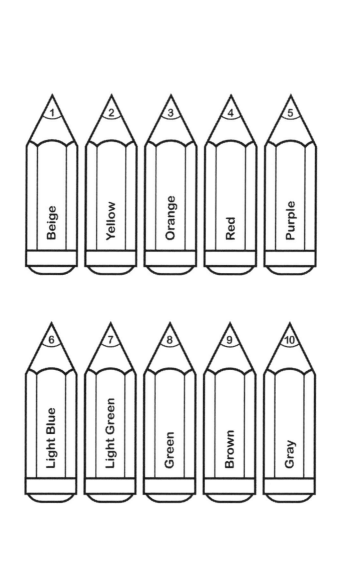

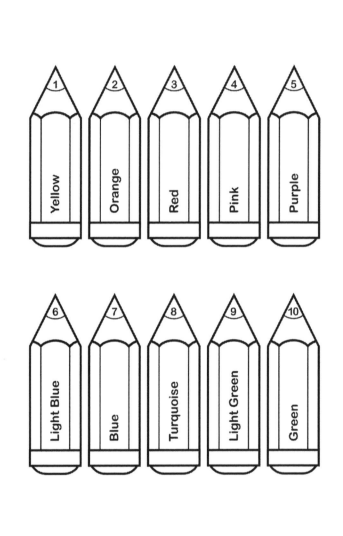

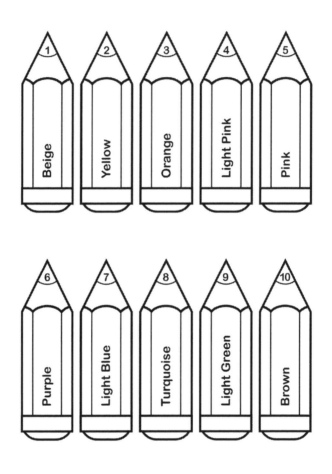

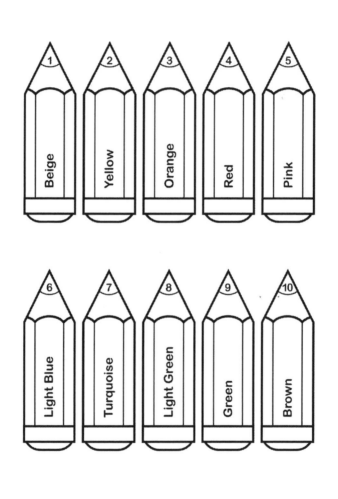

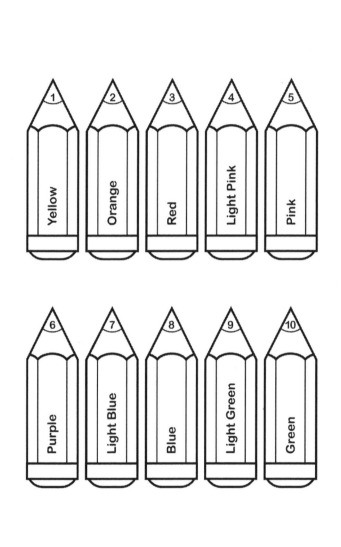

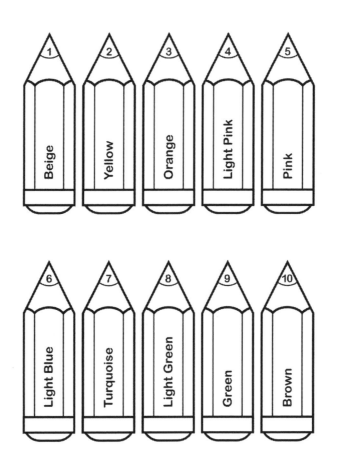

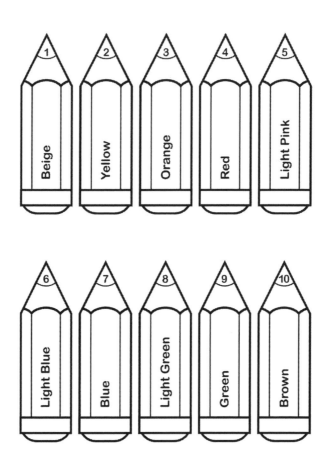

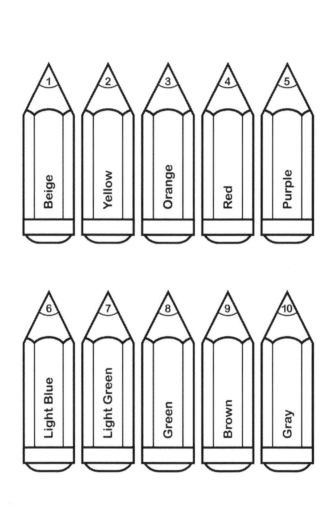

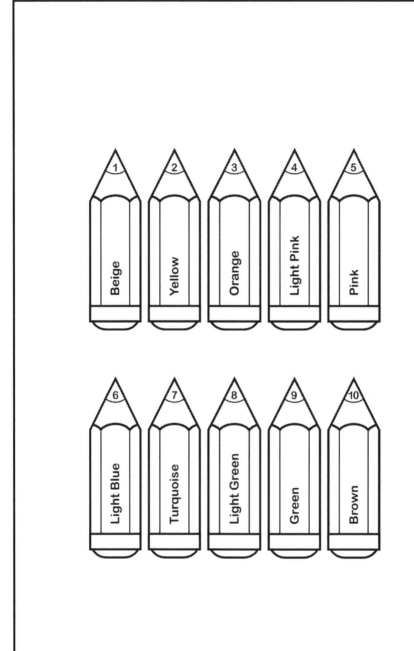

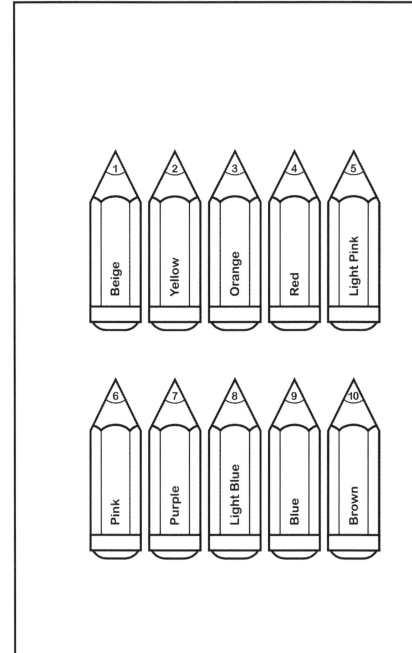

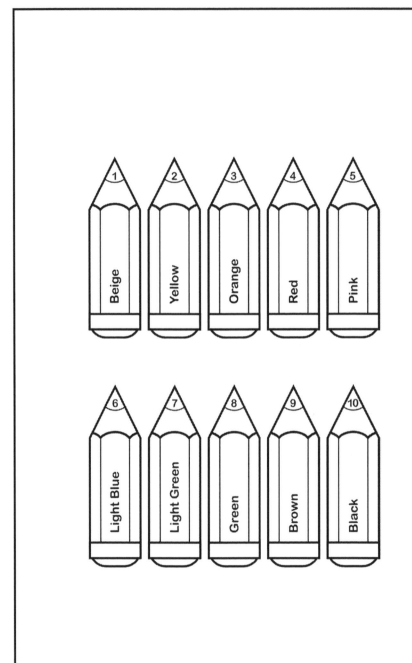

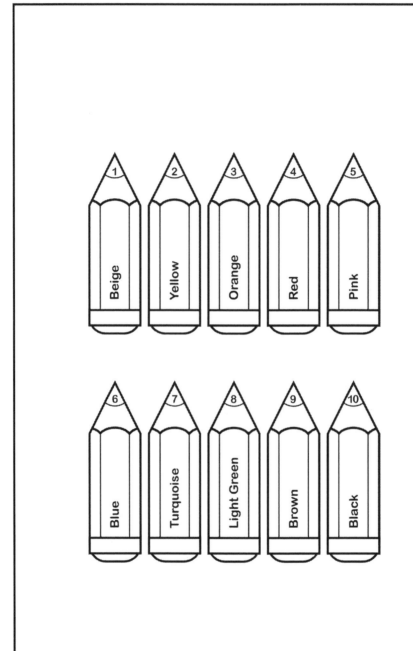

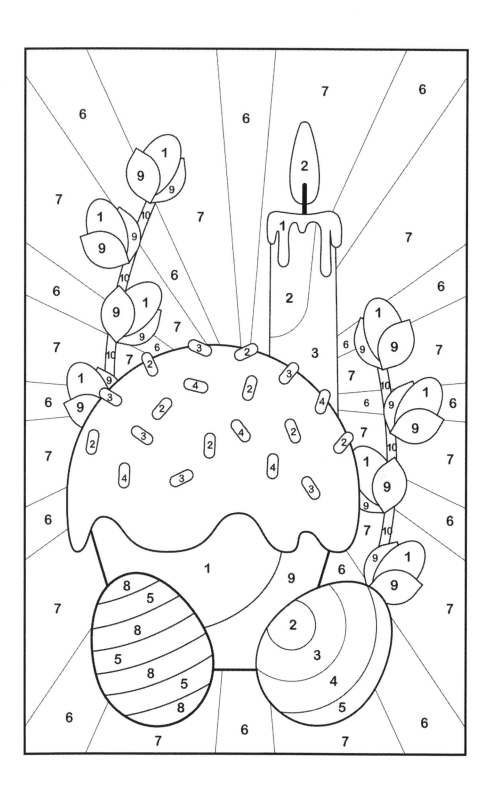

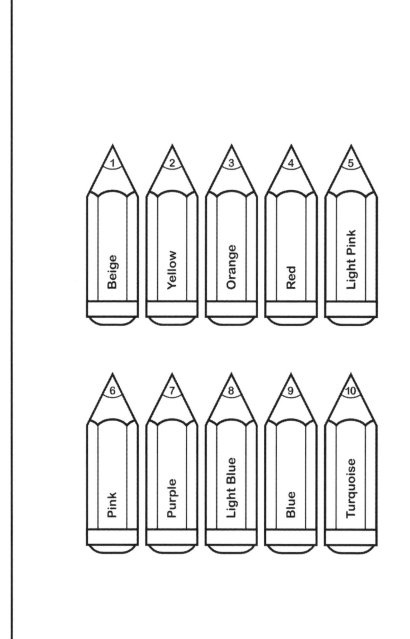

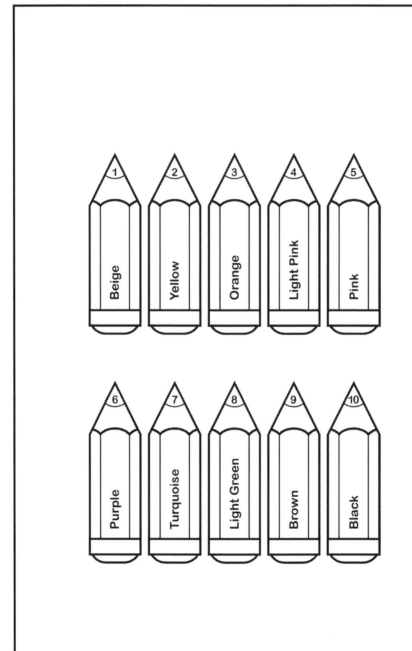

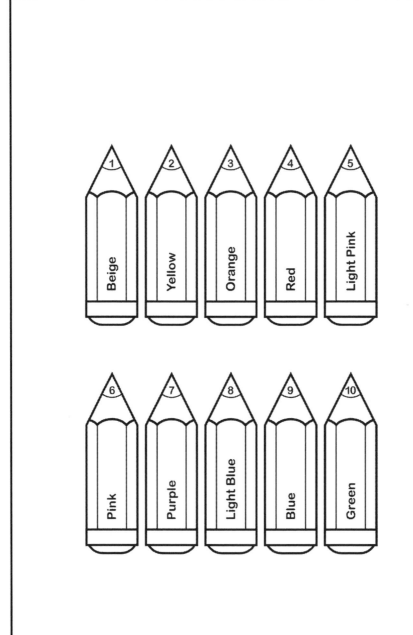

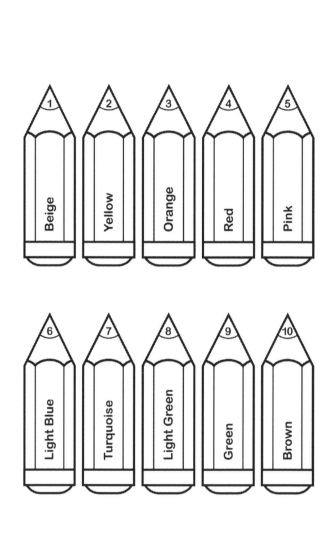

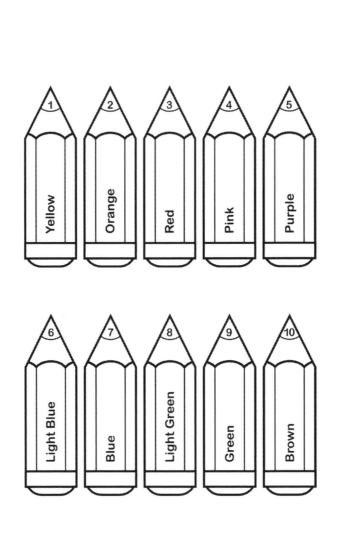

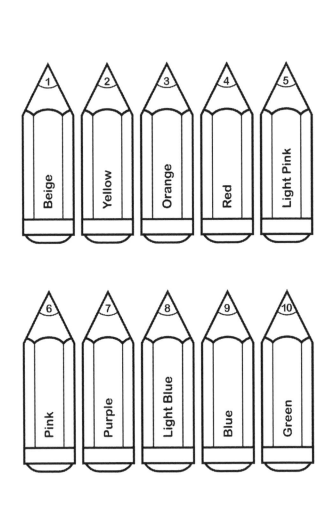

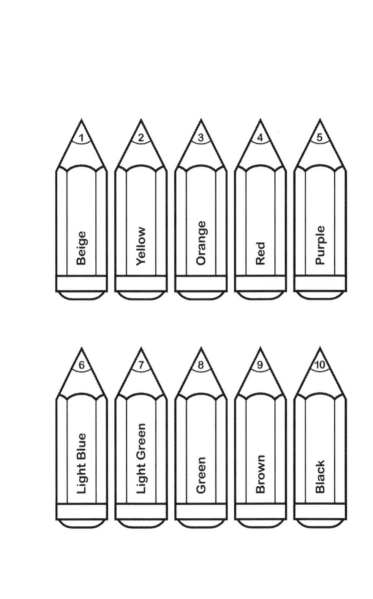

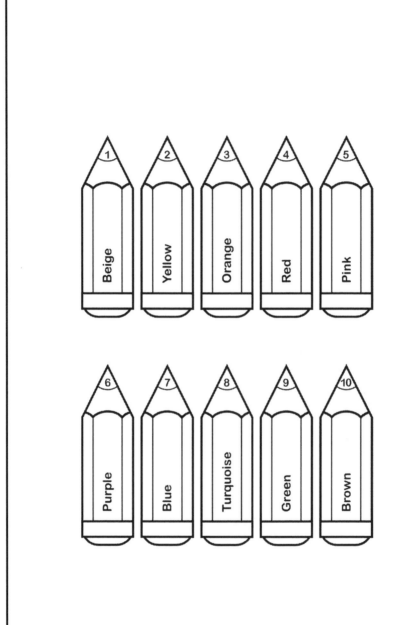

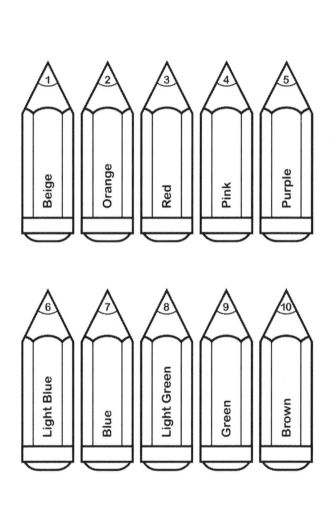

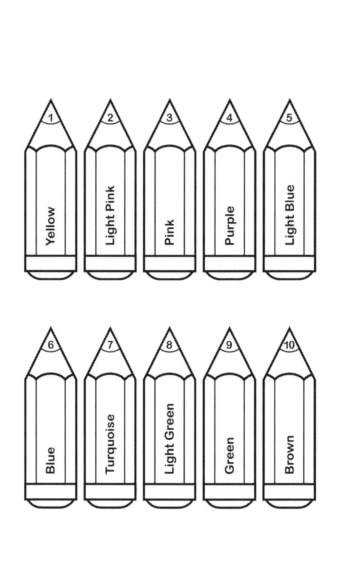

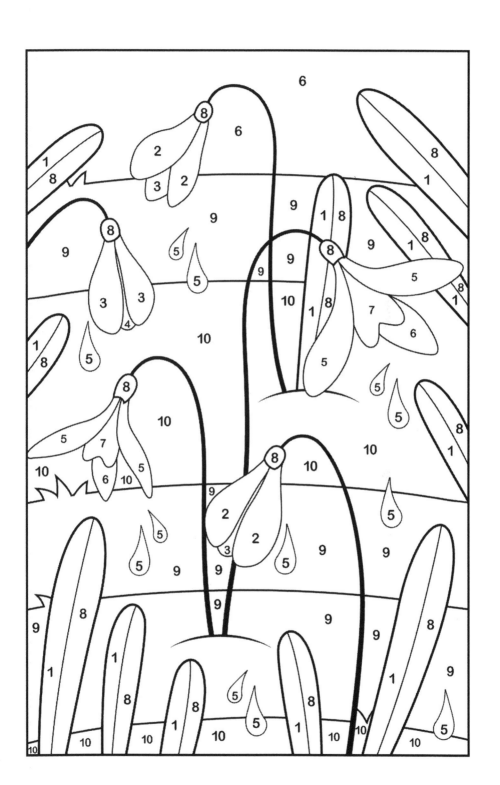

WOW! Great Work!

You did it! You colored in all of the Easter
pictures and brought all of the pages to life.

If you enjoyed completing this book, we would
love to hear about it. You can do this by leaving
a review wherever you purchased this book.
We love getting feedback from our little colorers!

Thank you very much, and have an
awesome day!

*Solution to the Bonus Question:
There are 38 Easter eggs inside this book.

Solution to the Bonus Question:

There are 38 Easter eggs inside
this book :-)

Made in the USA
Columbia, SC
24 February 2023

12948029R00041